Theory Paper Grade 2 2019 A

Duration 1½ hours

**TOTAL MARKS
100**

Candidates should answer ALL questions.
Write your answers on this paper — no others will be accepted.
Answers must be written clearly and neatly — otherwise marks may be lost.

1 Add the time signature to each of these five melodies.

10

2 Rewrite this melody, grouping (beaming) the notes correctly.

10

3 Answer **both** (a) and (b).

(a) Give the letter name of each of the notes marked ∗, including the sharp or flat sign where necessary. The first answer is given.

D
....

(b) How many semiquavers (16th notes) is the last note of the melody worth? ....

4 Name each key as shown by its key signature. The first answer is given.

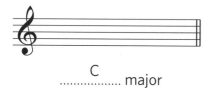      

........C........ major   .... minor   .... major

.... major   .... major   .... minor

5 Add the correct clef and any necessary accidentals to make each of the scales named below. Do **not** use key signatures.

D major

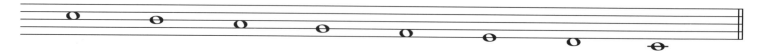

E minor

Which form of the minor scale have you used? ....

3.50

Music Theory Practice Papers 2019

ABRSM Grade 2

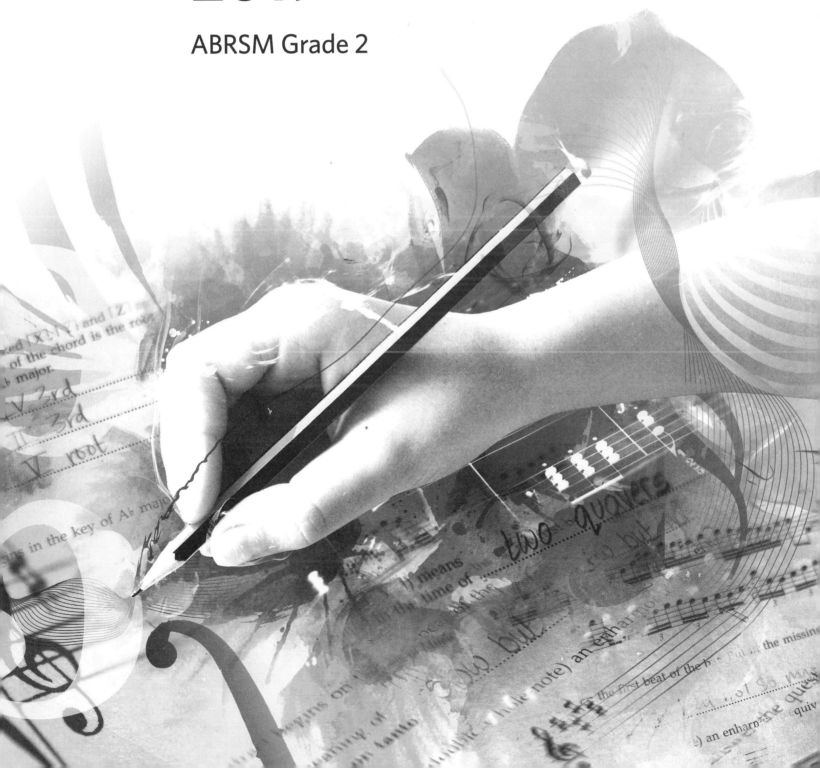

Music Theory Practice Papers 2019

ABRSM's *Music Theory Practice Papers 2019* are based on the 2019 Music Theory exam papers. The questions are the same as those used in recent exams.

Find out more about our Music Theory exams at **www.abrsm.org/theory**.

6 Give the number (e.g. 2nd, 3rd) of each of these melodic intervals, as shown in the first answer. The key is B♭ major.

5th
....

....

....

....

....

....

7 Rewrite this melody in the treble clef, keeping the pitch the same. The first bar is given.

8 Tick one box for each term, as shown in the first answer.

tenuto means:

held	✔
too much	☐
speed, time	☐
slow	☐

Vivace means:

at a medium speed	☐
fairly quick	☐
gradually getting quicker	☐
lively, quick	☐

molto means:

less	☐
more	☐
very, much	☐
movement	☐

fp means:

loud, then immediately quiet	☐
loud, gradually getting quieter	☐
quiet, gradually getting louder	☐
quiet, then immediately loud	☐

Larghetto means:

smoothly	☐
very slow, solemn	☐
rather slow	☐
gradually getting slower	☐

dolce means:

playful	☐
sweet	☐
merry	☐
stately	☐

9 Look at this melody and then answer the questions below.

Write your answer to question (b) on the stave below.

(a) (i) Answer TRUE or FALSE to this sentence:

All the notes in bars 1–4 of this
melody can be found in the key of C major. ....

(ii) Complete this sentence:

The triplet (♪♪♪) in bar 7 means
three quavers (eighth notes) in the time of ....

(iii) Give the time name (e.g. crotchet or
quarter note) of the **longest** note in the melody. ....

(iv) In which bar is the player told to pause or hold on to a note? Bar ....

(v) Give the number of the bar that will sound the **loudest**. Bar ....

(b) Copy out the music from the start of bar 1 to the end of bar 4, exactly as it is written above.
Don't forget the clef, time signature, tempo marking, dynamics and all other details. Write
the music on the blank stave above question (a).

Theory Paper   Grade 2   2019   B

Duration 1½ hours

TOTAL MARKS
100

Candidates should answer ALL questions.
Write your answers on this paper — no others will be accepted.
Answers must be written clearly and neatly — otherwise marks may be lost.

1 Add the missing bar-lines to these two melodies. The first bar-line is given in each.

10

2 Add the correct rest(s) at the places marked ＊ in these two melodies to make each bar complete.  10

3 Rewrite this melody in the bass clef, keeping the pitch the same. The first bar is given.

4 Answer **both** (a) and (b).

(a) Name the degree of the scale (e.g. 2nd, 3rd) of each of the notes marked ∗, as shown in the first answer. The key is E♭ major.

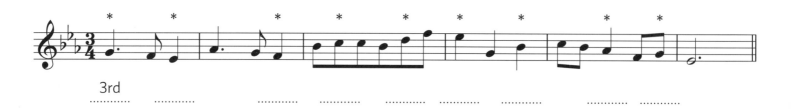

3rd
....

(b) Give the letter name of the **highest** note in the melody. ....

5 Using semibreves (whole notes), write one octave of the scales named below.

A minor, ascending, **without** key signature but adding any necessary accidentals.

Which form of the minor scale have you used? ....

B♭ major, descending, **with** key signature.

6 **After** each note write a **higher** note to form the named **melodic** interval within the key of G major. The first answer is given.

10

4th

2nd

3rd

5th

8th/8ve

7th

7 Add the correct clef and key signature to each of these tonic triads.

10

D major

Eb major

A minor

G major

E minor

8 Tick one box for each term/sign, as shown in the first answer.

10

means:

slur: detached	☐
slur: perform smoothly	✔
tie: detached	☐
tie: hold for the value of both notes	☐

giocoso means:

with movement	☐
lively, quick	☐
playful, merry	☐
majestic	☐

pp means:

very quiet	☐
quiet	☐
very loud	☐
moderately quiet	☐

means:

gradually getting louder	☐
gradually getting quieter	☐
gradually getting quicker	☐
loud	☐

means:

strong accent	☐
staccatissimo	☐
slight pressure	☐
sforzando	☐

Largo means:

very slow, solemn	☐
at a medium speed	☐
rather slow	☐
slow, stately	☐

9 Look at this melody and then answer the questions below.

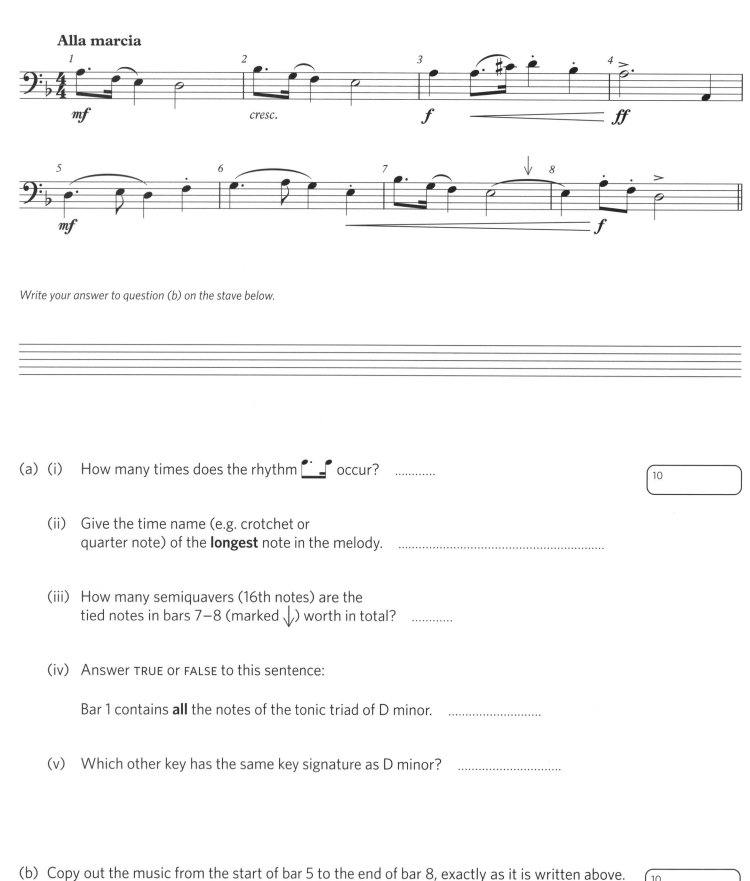

Write your answer to question (b) on the stave below.

(a) (i) How many times does the rhythm ♪. ♪ occur? ....

  10

   (ii) Give the time name (e.g. crotchet or
        quarter note) of the **longest** note in the melody. ....

   (iii) How many semiquavers (16th notes) are the
         tied notes in bars 7–8 (marked ↓) worth in total? ....

   (iv) Answer TRUE or FALSE to this sentence:

        Bar 1 contains **all** the notes of the tonic triad of D minor. ....

   (v) Which other key has the same key signature as D minor? ....

(b) Copy out the music from the start of bar 5 to the end of bar 8, exactly as it is written above.
    Don't forget the clef, key signature, dynamics and all other details. Write the music on the
    blank stave above question (a).

  10

Theory Paper   Grade 2   2019   C

Duration 1½ hours

TOTAL MARKS
100

Candidates should answer **ALL** questions.
Write your answers on this paper – no others will be accepted.
Answers must be written clearly and neatly – otherwise marks may be lost.

1   Add the time signature to each of these five melodies.

10

2   Answer **both** (a) and (b).

10

(a) Rewrite these treble-clef notes in the bass clef, keeping the pitch the same.
The first answer is given.

(b) In which major key are **all** these notes found?   ....

3 Add the correct clef to make each of these named notes. The first answer is given. `[10]`

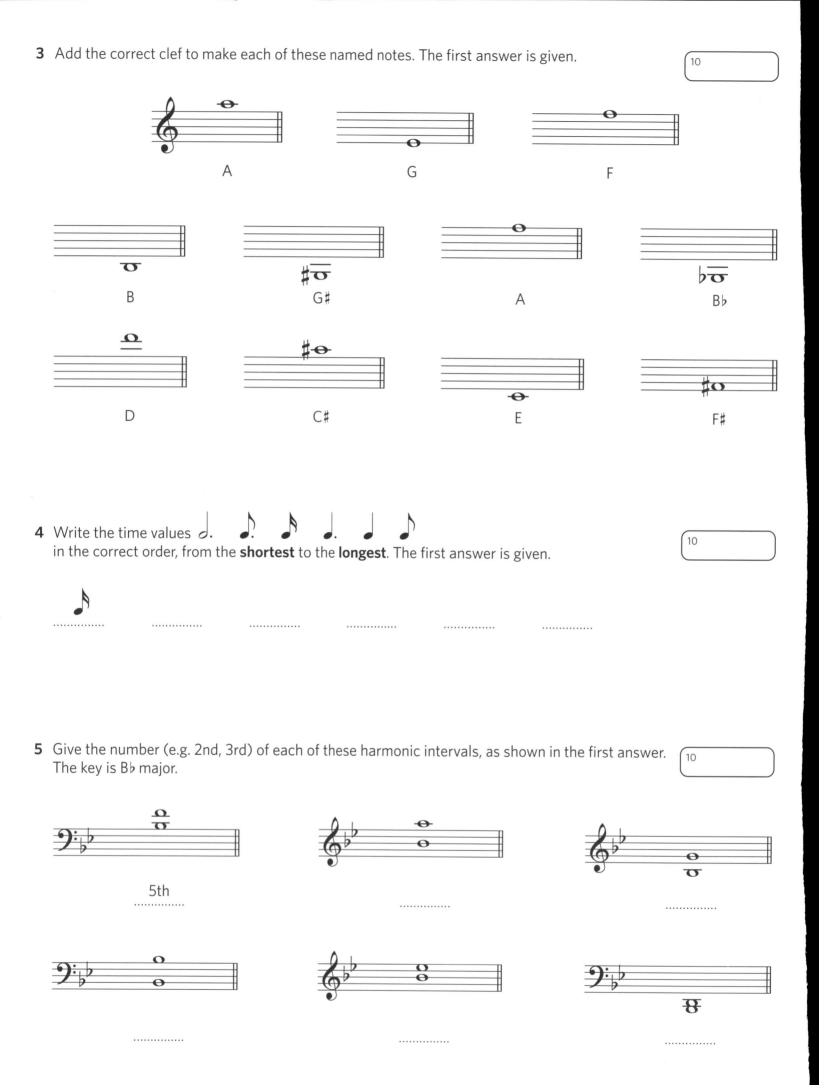

4 Write the time values ♩. ♪. ♪ ♩. ♩ ♪ in the correct order, from the **shortest** to the **longest**. The first answer is given. `[10]`

5 Give the number (e.g. 2nd, 3rd) of each of these harmonic intervals, as shown in the first answer. The key is B♭ major. `[10]`

5th

6 Write the tonic triads named below. Do **not** use key signatures but remember to add any necessary accidentals.

F major

A minor

D major

Eb major

E minor

7 Rewrite this melody using notes of **half the value**, beginning as shown. Remember to group (beam) the notes correctly where necessary.

8 Tick one box for each term, as shown in the first answer.

cantabile means:

in a singing style	✔
at a medium speed	☐
repeat from the beginning	☐
smoothly	☐

Presto means:

slow	☐
rather slow	☐
fast	☐
broadening	☐

grazioso means:

playful, merry	☐
graceful	☐
sweet	☐
expressive	☐

ff means:

gradually getting louder	☐
loud	☐
moderately loud	☐
very loud	☐

sostenuto means:

sustained	☐
detached	☐
held back	☐
in the style of	☐

con moto means:

with movement	☐
without movement	☐
less movement	☐
more movement	☐

9 Look at this melody and then answer the questions below.

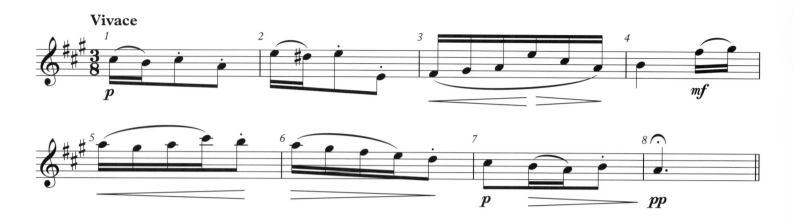

Write your answer to question (b) on the stave below.

(a) (i) Give the number of a bar that contains
all the notes of the tonic triad of A major.   Bar ....

(ii) How many times does the rhythm occur?   ....

(iii) Give the letter name of the **highest** note in
the melody, including the sharp sign if necessary.   ....

(iv) Answer TRUE or FALSE to this sentence:

$\frac{3}{8}$ means three quaver (eighth-note) beats in a bar.   ....

(v) In which bar is the player told to pause or hold on to a note?   Bar ....

(b) Copy out the music from the start of bar 5 to the end of bar 8, exactly as it is written above.
Don't forget the clef, key signature, dynamics and all other details. Write the music on the
blank stave above question (a).

Theory Paper   Grade 2   2019   S

Duration 1½ hours

TOTAL MARKS
100

Candidates should answer ALL questions.
Write your answers on this paper – no others will be accepted.
Answers must be written clearly and neatly – otherwise marks may be lost.

1 Add the missing bar-lines to these two melodies. The first bar-line is given in each.

10

2 Add the correct rest(s) at the places marked * in these two melodies to make each bar complete.

10

3 Rewrite this melody using notes of **twice the value**, beginning as shown.
Remember to group (beam) the notes correctly where necessary.

4 Answer **both** (a) and (b).

   (a) Rewrite these bass-clef notes in the treble clef, keeping the pitch the same.
The first answer is given.

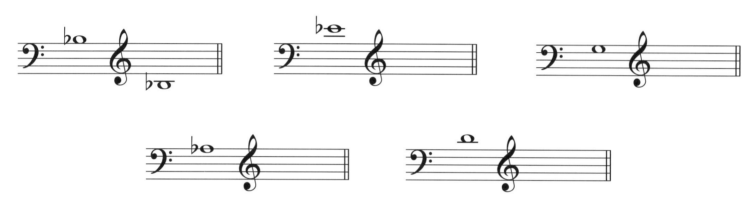

   (b) In which major key are **all** these notes found?   ....

5 Add the correct clef and any necessary accidentals to make each of the tonic triads named below. Do **not** use key signatures.

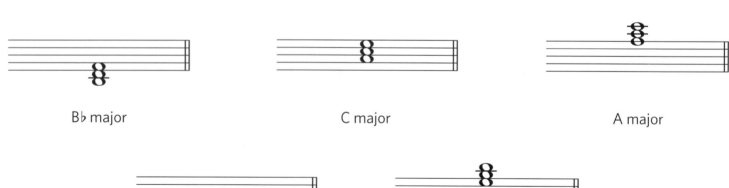

16

6 **Above** each note write a **higher** note to form the named **harmonic** interval within the key of A major. The first answer is given.

8th/8ve   6th   3rd

5th   4th   7th

10

7 Write the time values in the correct order, from the **longest** to the **shortest**. The first answer is given.

10

....

8 Tick one box for each term/sign, as shown in the first answer.

10

⎯⎯⎯⎯ means:

gradually getting louder ☐
gradually getting slower ☐
gradually getting quicker ☐
gradually getting quieter ✔

simile means:

in the style of ☐
sustained ☐
in the same way ☐
without ☐

Grave means:

very slow, solemn ☐
slower ☐
held back ☐
expressive ☐

allargando means:

rather slow ☐
in time ☐
slow, stately ☐
broadening ☐

non troppo means:

very much ☐
not too much ☐
too much ☐
not in time ☐

means:

staccatissimo ☐
smoothly ☐
forced, accented ☐
slightly separated ☐

9 Look at this melody and then answer the questions below.

Write your answer to question (b) on the stave below.

(a) (i) Give the number of a bar that contains
all the notes of the tonic triad of A minor.   Bar ....

  10

(ii) Give the time name (e.g. crotchet or
quarter note) of the **shortest rest** in the melody.   ....

(iii) Which other key has the same key signature as A minor?   ....

(iv) Answer TRUE or FALSE to this sentence:

  $\frac{3}{4}$ means three quaver (eighth-note) beats in a bar.   ....

(v) Give the number of the bar that contains the **quietest** note.   Bar ....

(b) Copy out the music from the start of bar 5 to the end of bar 8, exactly as it is written above.
Don't forget the clef, dynamics and all other details. Write the music on the blank stave
above question (a).

  10

Music Theory Practice Papers 2019

Four separate papers from ABRSM's 2019 Theory exams for Grade 2

- Essential practice material for all ABRSM Theory exam candidates
- Model answers also available

Support material for ABRSM Music Theory exams

Supporting the teaching and learning of music
in partnership with four Royal Schools of Music

Royal Academy of Music | Royal College of Music
Royal Northern College of Music | Royal Conservatoire of Scotland

www.abrsm.org f facebook.com/abrsm
🐦 @abrsm ▶ ABRSM YouTube

ISBN 978-1-78601-366-8